First Experiences

Lucy Moves House

Written by **Barbara Taylor Cork**
Illustrated by **Siobhan Dodds**

BRIMAX

This is Lucy and her brother, Tom. Soon they are moving to a new house.

A family has come to look around their old house. Mother shows them around and takes them upstairs to see the bedrooms.

When the family have gone, Lucy feels sad and cross. "I don't want anyone else to sleep in my room," she says grumpily. "Cheer up," says Mother. "In the new house, you'll have a bedroom of your very own."

"Would you like to go and see the new house?" asks Father. "We need to talk to the owners." "Yes please," says Lucy, running to the car. On the way, they pass a big park. The playground is full of children.

At the new house, the owner shows Lucy and Tom their bedrooms. "Your bed will fit in this corner," Mother says to Lucy, "and there's lots of room for your toys."

Today is Lucy's last day at playgroup. The children and the teacher give her a farewell present.

Lucy and her friend Sally are sad to say goodbye. "Sally can come and visit us in our new house, very soon," Mother tells Lucy.

When they get home, Tom and Father
are busy packing things into
big boxes.

Lucy helps Mother sort out her old clothes.
"I never wear these," says Mother.
"Put them in a pile to give away."

On moving day, Lucy and Tom wake up early.
The removal men arrive with a big van.

The two men, Bill and Fred, help the family pack everything into boxes. Bill wraps the glasses in paper, so that they won't break during the move.

Bill and Fred carry the heavy furniture and boxes to the van. When the house is empty, it doesn't look like Lucy and Tom's home anymore.

Mother puts Fluff, the cat, into her basket and takes her to the car. "Off we go," says Father, cheerfully. The children wave goodbye to their old house.

At the new house, Lucy and Tom are very excited. Their footsteps sound very loud when they run around the empty rooms.

"Come and have lunch before the van arrives,"
says Mother, unpacking the picnic she has made.
They sit on the floor to eat.

Soon Bill and Fred arrive in the van. Mother tells them where to put things.

When the boxes are unpacked, the children think the new house begins to feel like home.

Mother and Father are very tired. Moving house is hard work. They have a rest and a cup of tea.

Lucy and Tom go outside to play. The garden is much bigger than their old one. Tom really likes it.

But Lucy isn't happy. The new house and garden feel strange, and she misses her friend, Sally.

"Time for bed," calls Mother. "You're sharing a bedroom tonight." Lucy is pleased that she won't be sleeping on her own. Perhaps she will tomorrow night.

With their own beds and some of their toys, the bedroom feels almost like their old room. "We'll unpack the rest of your things in the morning," says Mother, kissing Lucy and Tom goodnight.

The next morning, the doorbell rings. "Is this your cat?" asks a little girl. "I found her in my garden. I'm Amy and I live next door."
"Yes, that's Fluff," says Lucy. "Thank you."

Lucy invites Amy to see her new bedroom.
"What a lovely room," says Amy, "and look at all
your toys. I'm glad you've come to live next door."
"So am I," says Lucy, smiling at her new friend.